PUMP
MAMA
PUMP

PUMP
MAMA
PUMP

RAEQUAEL PATTERSON

TABLE OF CONTENTS

Acknowledgements

This book is dedicated to every pumping/nursing mama out there. Your resilience and perseverance is to be commended. Not everyone is able to stick with this but you're taking it day by day and rocking it out! Keep pumping mama!

There is no way possible for me to write a book about pumping without thanking my wonderful husband, Jonathan and sons, Israel and Judah, who made me a mama and supported me through this great journey of breastfeeding. I will forever be grateful for your understanding and compassion through every around-the-clock pump session! You guys rock!

To my sisters Ashley Gray and Stacey Gay who were my text buddies, support system and part of the pregnancy "trifecta" I love you guys and thank you for the daily motivation and empowerment!

To every nurse in the GBMC-NICU who encouraged me to pump every three hours and not give up even if I only had a drop of milk, I thank you!

Disclaimer

I am an everyday pumping mama that wants to share what I've found to be my truth about pumping. No lactation consultant here, just a mama that knows the pumping struggle!

Introduction

I had it all planned out. First comes love then comes marriage then comes me with the baby carriage…or so I thought! I was in no way prepared to go through what I thought was the hardest time getting pregnant! It didn't happen for me like it did for everyone else. I struggled for almost an entire year to get pregnant and it was a true struggle. Through many tears, disappointments, and negative pregnancy tests I kept trying hoping that one day there would be conception and I'd be able to give birth to a baby. My faith at times diminished as I watched others around me get pregnant while I was still barren. I questioned God and even went as far as to contact our local fertility clinic in hopes of receiving the answer I needed about what was going on. The specialist advised me that their clinic required women to try conceiving for one solid year before they would begin any testing or offer any support.

The nine months my husband and I had tried to get pregnant seemed like a year in my mind, but I understood their logic and just kept trying like the clinic advised. My husband was very supportive (poor man) as we tried each month during my time of ovulation (thanks to my handy phone app!) but still nothing. We even took a trip to exclusively rest and a-hem "take care of business." Even still, we returned home only to receive negative pregnancy results a few weeks later. I had become exhausted with the thought of pregnancy and honestly stopped trying at month ten. One Sunday evening at my year end mark, I was in my bathroom and decided to take a test. I wasn't sure why, but I just wanted to see if maybe I could have been pregnant this time. So I took the test and waited the recommended five minutes and to my surprise, I saw the faintest pink line ever! Immediately I began to question if this line could actually mean I was pregnant because of its faintness. Deciding that even the faintest line was a victory to be celebrated, I basked in the possibility that it had finally happened, and I now was going to be a mama! I told my husband—who didn't understand my ramblings about the faint line—that we were expecting! He told me to call my best friend, who happens to be a nurse, so we could get a confirmation. She came over along with my sister and confirmed the best news ever...I was going to be a mama!

Preparing for Mamahood

Over the next nine months, time would go so fast (which I can say now because while pregnant I honestly felt like time stood still) from doctor's appointments to baby flutters and belly rubs pregnancy was everything I could imagine and more! I ate almost everything imaginable and enjoyed every moment of being pampered and being told how beautiful I was by my circle of friends, family, and the ladies on staff at Target (that store was my second home and the staff was so supportive of me). Pregnancy was exciting as the baby and my body grew. I was in awe that I was getting ready to give birth to a tiny human. I was given the most lavish baby showers and was honored that so many people wanted to celebrate our growing family. We had it all planned out: we would take Lamaze, nursing/lactation and CPR classes because we wanted to be prepared for the baby's arrival. But little did I know, my baby had other plans.

On Sunday, May 14, 2016, Mother's Day and my graduation day to be exact, I decided at six o'clock in the morning that I would finish up my baby's nursery. I finally finished around 7:45 am and had to make a Target run to return a few things and make a purchase for the last additions to the room. On my way to the store, the unexpected happened. I was on the phone with my mom and I felt a gush of fluid. I knew it wasn't the sprinkle of pee that usually came as I laughed or sneezed. This was different! I said to my mom, "Uh oh, I think my water broke." She told me to go home immediately. I decided to ignore her request and continued to Target because I had things to purchase. As I arrived at Target, waters broken and all (I would not recommend this), I made my returns/purchases and returned home to tell my husband that my water broke. He didn't believe me and said that we should get dressed for church and then we could go to the hospital after that. I let him know that I was very serious, that an immediate hospital run was in order. We got dressed and went straight to the hospital and it was confirmed, my water broke and it was time to give birth to my baby!

After the nurses confirmed that my water had truly broken, the doctor advised me that I would have to be induced because my cervix hadn't dilated at all. I guess that meant no graduation or mother's day festivities for me! The next few hours would be the most painful as my contractions were synthetically induced. I labored for quite a while without pain medication and the only relief from the pain that I had was my husband's reassurance and the fact that I knew why it had to be done. When it would get worse I would call for help but there was nothing that could be done, we had to let it take its course. When my cervix finally dilated, and my contractions started, I called for an epidural—I just knew it was time to give birth. Boy, was I wrong. I would sit for hours anxiously awaiting my son's arrival.

I will never forget the intensity of my 24 hours of active labor. It seemed like forever, eating ice chips and enduring constant contractions! By the time it was time to push I was tired but ever so ready! The doctor came in and said, "It's the time you've been waiting for, let's push." So I saddled up and pushed with all my strength six times, helping our baby to make his entrance into the world. As soon as our baby was born, the craziest thing happened. After planning for a baby boy for the eight months, the nurse screamed out, "It's a girl." Everyone in the room looked shocked. No one could believe this happened! The doctor replied suddenly, "No, no, it's a boy. See?" So we all went back to enjoying the moment. I was finally able to hold my baby boy in my arms. I couldn't believe it, he was finally here. I only got a moment to enjoy his presence before he was rushed to the NICU to ensure that everything was okay since he was six weeks early. I didn't get to see him for a few hours because they wanted to let the epidural wear off, so I waited with great excitement to see my new little gift.

Over the next few hours I would be greeted by tons of people. Social workers, nurses, and doctors who all had the same question: are you breastfeeding? And so it began!

Since I wasn't able to take the nursing/lactation classes and hadn't done much research on the topic, I was new to the lingo and didn't quite know what I was signing up for. My baby was in the NICU and was placed on a feeding tube because he didn't have the ability to latch and suck just yet. So, what was I to do? The lactation specialist came the evening I gave birth and asked all sorts of questions that I had no answers to. It was my first baby and of course my first attempt at producing milk. She was extremely helpful with giving me the information I needed and did not add pressure to an already scary situation. She told me that since my baby was in the NICU it may be harder for him to suck but to try anyway. We walked up to the NICU and I was given the weirdest thing, a Medela Nipple Shield. I had seen one before but didn't understand why my baby wouldn't be able to just latch onto my breast. I asked no questions (which I regret) and attempted to nurse. He did not latch. I was a bit disappointed but understood that the baby was still getting accustomed to the world so I allowed the nurses to bottle feed him while I worked out in my mind what I would do.

One of the NICU nurses had an awesome suggestion. She said that it would be great if the baby could get some of the colostrum, the first few drops of milk my body produced . She explained that the colostrum is high in protein, vitamins, and antibodies but only lasted during the first couple of days before the breast milk actually came in. The expression of colostrum could be accomplished by pumping if he wouldn't latch on. I never heard of anyone pumping from the beginning, but she explained that this was normal. This nurse gave me so much hope as she pulled me to the side and said "Listen, I promise if you pump every three hours by my next shift, you will have some milk or at least drops that you can give to the baby." I needed that pep talk because I was certainly about to give up quickly. I went down to my room, sat on the side of the bed and began pumping.

A bit of encouragement before we get into all the pumping lingo and details. You've already experienced one of the greatest accomplishments in the world and that's having your precious baby! Please know that pumping/nursing takes an extreme amount of time, mental energy, and work. No one but you will truly understand the sacrifice you're about to make. There will be moments when you feel like giving up or even when the excuse of not pumping becomes greater than the actual act; make a choice and stick to it! Only you know what's good for your mental state and if pumping/nursing may not be, there are tons of options out there to supplement and give your little one the nutrition that they need. You're still a great mama either way! And if you're ever feeling alone, know that there are women all over the WORLD awake pumping with you, making the same sacrifice ☺

A Mama's First Impressions
of
"The PUMP"

What's this pumping stuff all about? Initially I had the same question. Why on earth would I be sitting still for 20-30 minutes every three hours to have a machine pull milk out of me? After all, I could just put the baby up to my breast and meet his demand with my supply! But for me and countless other mamas it wasn't that simple. As I sat on the bed looking at all these parts I had never seen before trying to put them together, I got a bit overwhelmed. So you mean I would have to clean all of this after I pump? This was one of my first thoughts. Even still, I proceeded to prepare the electric breast pump provided by the hospital (Just an FYI, the hospital provides a hospital grade pump while you are in the hospital, just be sure to contact your health insurance provider for the pump you will take home). When I connected the pump to my breast and began to feel the pull I marveled at how amazing women are. I was about to be a milk machine and I loved it. I set the alarm on my phone for 20 minutes and when the timer went off, I looked down at the bottles attached to the pump and there was nothing absolutely nothing—not one drop of colostrum or milk. At that very moment I told my husband that this pump life was not for me! How could I possibly work so hard to get nothing? He encouraged me and said, "Keep pumping baby, it will come." The next pumping session was scheduled for 12 o'clock midnight. I was exhausted and couldn't imagine that I'd be up every three hours to get drops of milk, but I did it for my baby. I got up to pump and to my surprise I had a few drops. I ran it up to the NICU, labeled the bottles, and placed it into the refrigerator.

Like me, you may have some crazy first impressions of pumping exclusively. Believe me, if it is your first time, you have all types of thoughts and questions. *Where will I pump? How often will I have to pump? Wait, I have to use all of these parts when I pump? Where will I store the milk? How long does the milk last? What will I do if the baby is not with me?* These are just some of the questions I had as I instantly became overwhelmed with the whole idea of pumping. Not to worry though, every mom has these questions and I will try to give you some insight on what I did to quiet these worrisome thoughts and prevent anxiety as best as I knew how. The reality is that having a baby and tending to their needs outside of feeding can be a little overwhelming in itself, so I'll try to relieve some of the stress that comes with feeding.

Fad vs. Lifestyle

Over the next few days, I would have to decide how committed to this lifestyle I really was going to be. I had to understand that whether pumping or breastfeeding, there would be a great deal of undisrupted time required in addition to the daily tasks of being a mom. Pumping alone deducts a great deal of time from your day because you not only have to pump but you have to clean parts and worry about milk storage. I've discovered that if you see pumping as something that's "trendy" and you are more concerned with how you will look as a mama if you don't give your baby your milk, you may not make it long! Fads as we know them are short-lived, they are eye-catching and seem appealing. Fads fade and, as it is with fashion, what's in one day can be a fashion fail the next. This is how pumping can be, initially it's appealing but when you realize how much time you have to invest to do it, that appeal begins to fade and you are faced with the question: "Why am I doing this?" As rhetorical as the question may seem I am sure that many pumping mamas have been faced with this question. Most times we know the benefits of pumping but in some moments the reality of what you are doing becomes fatiguing and you literally may not feel like pumping anymore, that's when the lifestyle of pumping comes into play.

Whatever you do that brings a sense of normalcy in your day-to-day life is a part of your lifestyle. At 12 months in I can honestly say that pumping has become a lifestyle for me. There are moments when I'm done with it and I pale at the fact that it's time to pump, but I do it because it's a part of me for now at least. I've adapted to this pump life and until the time comes to stop pumping, a mama's gotta do what mama's gotta do! I remind myself daily of the rewards of pumping for my baby, the financial benefits, and my overall happiness about being able to produce milk for my little one. Many days you will be faced with the question from friends, family, co-workers, and random people of when you'll stop pumping. Honestly, that question alone can make you cringe or in your mind want to bop them on the head (just kidding), but I've learned that with this lifestyle you have to bring people into your world and allow them to know where you are coming from. No, you don't owe anyone an explanation, but you also do not owe yourself the constant internal defense it takes to deal with questions about your choice to pump beyond what they deem a reasonable timeframe! Say your truth to people and be settled with it.

Pumping Exclusively

Just the decision to be a nursing mom means you have chosen to be committed to feeding your baby breastmilk. Please do not let anyone tell you that pumping is not considered breastfeeding because it definitely is. Pumping, however, requires a bit more than nursing. From the time you start, it's recommended that you pump 8 to 12 times per day which is as often as a nursing mom would nurse their baby. You may want to pump every time your baby eats. In this case, you give the baby the bottle, clean their diaper and run to get your pump. As stated previously, I pumped every three hours, eight times a day, and for 20-25 minutes per session. Once you develop a routine, it makes it much easier to grasp this lifestyle change. One of the major things that has helped me is not being restricted to the pumping only at home. What does that mean? I multitask. I am not one that can just sit still with a pump attached to me while doing nothing but holding the bottle attachments while pumping. That would get boring to me really quickly. When I decided I was going to be an exclusive pumper, I invested in a hands-free bra so I could accomplish other tasks while carrying the pump around with me. I literally was able to do everything from driving to folding laundry to cooking dinner and even writing this book. The hands-free bra that I chose was by Medela but after looking on Pinterest, I realized that I could take a sports bra and cut two holes in the area of the nipple to yield the same results of the hands-free bra for a total savings of more than $25.00! For the first few months I used a hands-free bra but then I became what I thought was a pump pro and just put the flanges under my nursing bra and used the underwire to hold them on. I would not recommend this initially because you risk spilling the milk and we all know that spilled milk is enough to make a mama cry. Don't get discouraged by the number or times you have to pump initially, this will change as your baby grows.

Pump Parts

While spilled milk can bring a mama to tears, milk pumped through and into dirty pump parts can make baby ill. Although sterilization of pump parts between sessions can be exhausting, especially to a new mom, it is essential. Each time that you pump you have to make sure that the pump parts are cleaned for the next pumping session. This can be tedious if you are pumping through the night or if you just don't feel like cleaning all those parts. My fellow pumping mamas and I discovered that you can refrigerate or freeze pump parts in a sandwich bag between sessions so they would remain sterile. I have opted to do this a few times but did not continue this practice because something about it was not sanitary to me. Instead I would wash and dry parts immediately after or right before pumping. I have also purchased additional parts to use when I am out so that I do not feel the pressure of having to clean parts when I am not home. Some moms ask for help from their spouse to clean the pump parts, I did not do this because I was super particular on how I wanted the pump parts washed and sterilized.

After a while, though, I needed to find a better and more efficient way to pump and store my breastmilk. Thankfully, we live in an age of innovation and most of the things that we know we need or have no clue of are at our fingertips. A few months into my pumping journey, I received an innovative breastmilk storage system. The Kiinde Breast Milk Storage System provides you with the pump adapters needed to use your pump and store your milk in their storage bags. I do prefer and highly recommend this system because it makes cleaning easier as you pump directly into the Kiinde bags, place the bag directly into the Kiinde bottle and attach the nipple. This is super easy. The bags can get a little pricey but for the convenience it is definitely worth it. You can freeze the bags and save them for when you need them. Not only does it save time for cleaning bottles, but it also reduces spills from pouring the milk from traditional storage bags to the bottle. Depending on how you want to store your milk, there are many options that may be right for you to purchase both online and in-store.

As you pump, you will notice that you may have to replace certain parts like the flanges (breast shield) or the pump valves. It is important to know when you need to change both. The flange is the piece that is held to your breast when you are pumping. The flow of your milk is optimized when you have the proper size flange. A flange that is too large will engage more of your areola and cause discomfort because of the rubbing against the flange. A flange that is too small will engage your entire nipple and cause it to rub against the side of the flange. Both a too small or too big flange will cause discomfort and could affect milk production.

When it comes to pump valves, it is important to change them every two to three months. You will notice a difference in suction if you do not change them which will affect the amount of milk that is extracted. Don't get discouraged though because when they are changed, you will see an increase in the amount of milk that you extract.

One of the least of your worries is tubing. Although you should clean them, you don't have to replace them unless you just want new tubing. Lastly, over time, you may notice that your pump is not extracting as much milk as it did when you first started pumping. This can be due to pump parts or the fact that you need a new pump. I would recommend contacting the manufacturer first and if there is nothing that they can do about it, you may want to purchase a replacement pump. I have had to do this during my time of pumping and have tried many pumps which we will discuss in a later chapter.

On-the-Go Mama

As I stated before, I did not enjoy being stuck to my pump, unable to accomplish anything while the pump was doing its job. This didn't just pertain to being inside the house, however, because I lead a busy life. I've discovered that pumping on the go is possible! Having everything you need while pumping on the go helps to greatly reduce stress and frustration. If you have your pump bag set up the night before a busy day, you won't have to worry about leaving the essentials. I make sure to pack a manual pump (Medela) just in case, Milk-Maid tea, pump parts, milk storage bags, zip lock bags for dirty pump parts, a few napkins, nipple cream (Lansinoh), nursing pads, and a nursing cover just in case I have to pump out in the open. I usually don't have to take this stuff out of the bag unless it has to be cleaned (pump parts). I always like to make sure I have everything I need to be prepared because there have been times when I have been missing flanges or other pump parts and was unable to pump or had to make a Target run to purchase missing parts.

If at all possible, purchase a pump with rechargeable batteries or one that can take batteries. I am a mama that pumps on the go and I can't have anything holding me back. In the very beginning, my husband and I were looking to purchase a new home so we had to travel extensively. He purchased me a car adapter which allowed me to plug in the pump and pump while he was driving. Needless to say I would pump on the way to work, church, on flights, friend's homes, etc. Now this may not be the safest thing to do if you're driving (so focus on the road) but if you're the passenger, pump on mama!

The Pumping, Working Mama

As if pumping doesn't have its own stressors, adding work into the equation poses an additional stress. *Will I have time to pump, where will I pump, how often and long can I pump, what should I bring to work daily, what should I leave at work?* I had all of these questions leading up to my return from maternity leave. I decided a few nights before my first day back to make sure that I had all of the essentials for pumping away from home. All I needed to add to the bag the morning of work was the pump itself. I think being acquainted with pumping away from home calmed my nervousness about pumping in public. My biggest concern was the amount of time I would be allotted to pump while on the clock.

Some mamas are unaware that there are laws that protect you if you're nursing! You should not feel like you have to choose between your work and feeding your baby. That's a no-no. When you return back to work, you may be covered by The Affordable Care Act also known as "Obamacare" Section 4207. If you are covered by this law, your employer is required to provide you with a "reasonable break time" to pump as well as a private space to do so. It is my advice, however, to speak with the Human Resources department at your place of employment ahead of time to see what options are available. You should not have to go through an entire day uncomfortable and unable to pump since this is the primary means by which your baby eats. If you do happen to have a stressful work environment, it is still important to pump. I've read that many moms stop pumping when they return back to work because of the stress related to not being able to take time away from duties, no storage for milk, or no conducive environment for pumping. What I would suggest is if there's no space is that you speak with management to create it.

I'm not a bathroom pumping mama because of my germ issues but some mamas don't mind it. If that's you, make it as sanitary as you can and get that milk out! Always make sure you have a cooler or something to store the milk for the time that you are away from home, preferably somewhere it can be locked up so that there's no possibility of theft or contamination. Theft sounds funny right? True story: one day I left my milk at work and it was gone the next day. I am not sure who took my sweet almondy tasting breastmilk but I'm sure they were in for a surprise when they couldn't get past the fat plug at the top! I should have reported it but I didn't because I knew later in life I'd write it in my book! Returning back to work can be hard but pumping at work doesn't have to be. Know your rights and have your employer come up to the standard.

Finding a Place to Pump

My pump and I have been everywhere together (except the bathroom). We have formed a bond that will not be broken until the day that I take my last pump or it decides to stop working. My insurance company gave me the Ameda Purely Yours pump (which we will discuss in a later chapter`) and I was able to take it with me wherever I went. There was no place where I didn't pump! I had no restrictions. I pumped at church, in the car, at the park, even at IKEA. I was a limitless pumping mama. As long as I had batteries or a charger I was pumping. Pumping had become part of my lifestyle and to make sure that I was not engorged, I made it a habit of pumping consistently. Just make sure you are comfortable with where you are. People will not understand it just like they don't understand nursing, but again you're doing what you have to do and that's feeding your baby!

I was able to pump so freely because of the versatility of my pump. Some pumps have the option to use batteries while others have to be connected to a power source. If you feel comfortable pumping in the car and your pump does not have a battery option, there are many car adapters available. The adapter I used was 100 watts, purchased on Amazon for a reasonable price. If you choose to pump using one of these devices in the car, please make sure that you are also using safety precautions which include checking your surroundings and not pumping while driving (I did but I wouldn't recommend it because it's not one of the safest things to do while driving).

No matter what, you have options, do not feel like you have to wait until you get back home to pump. Pump as much as you can, wherever you can!

Traveling while Pumping

I decided to surprise my husband with a mini-vacay to Montreal for his birthday. I booked a flight and hotel room and secured a sitter and was ready to go! What I had been missing though were the intricate details on how pumping would affect my travel. I hadn't really thought about it because I was so enthused about being able to go on a vacation. When I finally gathered myself I realized that pumping and traveling could make my trip stressful if I did not plan it right. I decided to do a little research to see what I could uncover about how airports/TSA handled pumps and milk storage. I began looking online and found some vague information about how the TSA would have to screen the milk to make sure that it was not anything hazardous or illegal. I was open to that because it would be my only means of getting the milk on the plane and there was no way that I was allowing my liquid gold to be considered a checked bag. According to tsa.gov you should notify the TSA Officer that you have breastmilk in your carry-on. What got me was the stipulation of "reasonable quantities." When I read that immediately I wondered what was reasonable and I decided to call TSA. I was advised that there really were no measurements on reasonable and that I would be able to take all of my pumped milk with me after screening and to keep it separate from my other belongings.

The TSA officers may ask you to open your containers to screen them but this is not generally done. If your breastmilk has to go through an X-ray screening like mine did because it was frozen, the Food and Drug Administration states that there are no known adverse effects on the milk screened using X-ray technology. Please note that your ice pack may be subject to the same screening as your breastmilk.

Now that the screening has been covered, let's discuss where you'll pump in the airport. I said it before and I'll say it again: pump anywhere you feel comfortable. At this point, I feel like Dr. Seuss, "I will pump here or there, I will pump everywhere." And I do. If you arrive early at the airport and have checked your bags you can pump at the gate just make sure you have everything you need, relax, and pump. I noticed that some gates have designated areas for nursing mamas which is very helpful. If you feel rushed once you get to the gate, take a breather and wait until you are ready even if that is not until you get on the plane. The only thing that does discourage me from pumping sometimes is the sound of the pump. I really don't want to make others uncomfortable with the noise, but if you're okay with it, pump mama.

When you travel make sure you have:

- Your pump and pump parts (flanges, extension cord, batteries, tubing)

- A water tight cooler

- Plenty of freezer packs

- Sufficient supply of milk storage bags/bottles

- Breast pads just in case of leakage

- A sharpie to mark the milk.

Please make sure that when booking your hotel you ask for a room with a freezer or if they have somewhere milk can be stored. You do not want to be away from home with nowhere to store your milk.

On your way back home, make sure that you pack your milk sufficiently and that the freezer packs are frozen. You want to make sure that all of your milk is in proximity of the freezer packs to ensure the milk does not thaw. If the milk does happen to partially thaw out, it can be refrozen. I do not refreeze milk that has been completely thawed out, instead I refrigerate it and use it within 24 hours. If your trip is greater than 24 hours, ask the flight attendant if they have any ice available and put it in a bag to make sure that your milk stays cold. When you get to your destination make sure that you freeze your milk if it hasn't thawed.

4 Truths and a Myth

Truth #1: Continuous pumping WILL increase supply

The more you pump the more milk you produce. You've read this on all the blogs, in books and on social media feeds but the truth is, all bodies are not created equal. And while some moms may pump and get an abundant supply, some moms may produce just enough for each feeding, or even have to supplement because their baby is still hungry. When your baby is first born your body has to adjust to what's transpired. Initially when your baby latches on, he or she is able to get the colostrum first and then the actual milk comes in. It seems like the more your body becomes acquainted with the need for milk, the more the body supplies it. For the first couple of weeks, our babies do not require as much milk, so our bodies aim to give them just enough. By week four or five our baby's requirements for milk increases to about three to four ounces per feeding and then you tend to see the demand for the supply put on your production. Our bodies naturally produce the milk that our babies need, and it should be a sufficient supply, but some mamas just do not produce enough. When this happens it becomes discouraging and some feel the urge to stop pumping. Please don't stop, especially if you have not tried all the options available to assist with milk production.

Daily I am introduced to people who are pumping and have issues with it. I recommend natural stimulation first which includes increasing pumping through "power pumping" or natural supplements that I have tried. Some of these options work and some don't (this will be discussed in a later chapter). What I've found to be most helpful is getting that pump out and pumping more frequently which seemingly has the ability to reprogram your body and make your body believe that you "need" the milk. The more often you do it the better! I used to chuckle with my girlfriends about how I trick my body into production, and how my milk was never really regulated by the baby because I hardly nursed. My milk production was regulated by the pump and the more I pumped the more milk I got. The constant stimulation or pumping for longer periods of time should increase your flow so you may want to add another pump session or increase the time for each session. I know you're wondering how you can do that with your already busy schedule. Mama, the simple truth is you have to make the time to get your milk up. Your baby will thank you later! Whatever the cause for needing to pump more: decreased supply, wanting to increase your freezer stash or just wanting to provide enough milk for your baby, don't quit—especially if it's something you sincerely want to do.

Truth #2: Pumping after nursing is beneficial

This book is exclusively for pumping mamas but some of us try to see if the baby will still latch on from time to time. In those instances, if the baby does latch, he or she may not completely empty your breast or may become more accustomed to nursing from one breast which may leave milk in your other breast that needs to be extracted. After nursing, if you have extra time, it may be advantageous to pump the rest of the milk out of both breasts. This will not only give you a stash of milk for times when you may have a sitter or may be going out, but it will help to increase your milk supply. It may feel like double work but it helps with regulating how much milk you produce for your baby. When you have a little snacker who nurses for 5 minutes or 5 suck increments it may be a little harder to pump after nursing, I get it, but still try so that you can make your body believe that you always need the milk!

Truth #3: There are lifestyle factors that influence milk production

Stress

There are many things that contribute to the amount of milk that you get between pumping sessions or overall. Stress and your overall well-being can contribute to the abundance or lack of supply. Your body knows what it has to do but stress can "slow the flow." So when pumping, try to be as calm as possible. Whenever you're stressed your body releases cortisol, norepinephrine and adrenaline which help your body to cope with the stress. Cortisol has the ability to enter breastmilk and influence its contents which can cause some emotion to transfer to your little one. Reading calming books or listening to music that is calming can add to your pumping experience. Pumping in itself can become stressful but try not to let it. Focus on what comes first, your health and well-being and then disburse what's left to the tasks that you have for the day. Mama, you want to be as emotionally and mentally stable as possible for your baby and making sure that you take care of yourself is so important. If you are stressed right now, even while reading this book, it is my hope that you can take a few minutes to gather your thoughts, breathe and realize what it takes to make you okay in order to decrease those stress levels and increase your supply.

Menstrual Cycle

Some mamas do not have a menstrual cycle while breastfeeding/pumping, but if it creeps up on you, it is a common reason for decrease in supply. Generally a week or so prior to your cycle you will notice a decrease in milk supply. Again, this is common, but your milk supply should increase during or after your cycle. Keep up with your normal pumping schedule to ensure that there is no permanent issue with your production due to the decrease in simulation. Our bodies are pretty clever and it is my thought that they are trying to look out for our best interest! I came on my cycle six months postpartum and my milk decreased greatly! I went from pumping 13 ounces per pump session to 4.5 ounces per session which was not enough for my baby. The first time this happened I was in complete shock and I became stressed. I had no idea my cycle was coming at the time so I didn't know what to do. I read blogs, but because I had no symptoms besides the decrease in production, I didn't really get answers. When my cycle finally came a week later I remembered a blog I read and realized why there was a decrease. I kept pumping according to my regular schedule and midway through my cycle, my milk returned. Make sure you track your cycle to decrease your stress level related to milk production. At least you'll be able to rule out your cycle! Don't get discouraged, mama, your milk will be back even if you have to power pump or take a lactation supplement to do so.

The Time Dilemma

The golden rule of pumping is the more you pump the more you get (in some instances). If you are not pumping frequently, your body begins to think that you do not need the milk that it would ordinarily produce. Some moms may become engorged if they haven't pumped in a while which is an indicator that there needs to be some stimulation because the breasts are full. Unless you are attempting to stop the flow of your milk, please do not allow your breast to become engorged often. Engorgement happens when there is infrequent pumping or nursing or when there is an obstruction to your milk ducts. Engorgement can lead to many health concerns that are not worth the 10-20 minutes you could have pumped to mitigate the health issue. You can tell if your breast are engorged if you experience hard, swollen, uncomfortable to the touch breasts. This can cause fever and extreme discomfort for you but could also affect your milk production. I'm not saying that if you pump often you will not become engorged but it will lessen the likelihood for engorgement. If you become engorged, you can place a warm compress on your breast or take a warm shower before pumping. I have experienced engorgement in my early pumping months due to oversupply and not fully retrieving all of the milk that was in my breast. The discomfort was so painful that I wanted to go to the hospital to utilize the hospital grade pump or to release all of the milk. I found that massaging my breast in the shower under the warm water and using a single pumping method (utilizing the manual pump) for the breast helped me to release the milk and alleviate the engorgement.

If you do not have the time during the day to pump for an extensive period of time, you may want to pump for more sessions but for a decreased amount of time. When you have more time, you may be able to "power pump." Power pumping is when you pump incrementally with an on and off method. I have found this to be very beneficial for me during times of decreased supply. You basically choose a time of generally 10 minutes per breast and rest for 10 minutes and then pump again. This is a method you use if you have free time because you need to spend at least an hour doing it.

Truth #4: Lactation Supplements Work

There are many up and coming companies out there who have created lactation supplements. I have not tried many of them because of my over-supply but have heard through reviews that these supplements work. One supplement that I have tried is the organic MilkMaid tea by Earth Mama, Angel Baby Organics. This tea's ingredients are said to increase/boost supply. I can honestly say it worked for me on the days that my supply was not where it was supposed to be. I am not a consistent drinker of this tea, I just drank it when I had issues with my supply and it worked for me. I've also tried salmon, blue Gatorade (I am not sure if the color has anything to do with it), oatmeal and an increase in water intake. When trying these supplements, I was able to see an increase in my diminishing supply. I read reviews on these supplements prior to trying them on numerous websites and blogs and they actually worked. Above all, I believe that staying hydrated contributes to supply. Now remember, just because you drink a gallon of water you may not produce a gallon of milk, but your overall hydration will help with supply. I have read that fenugreek, a natural herb, also assists in milk production but I have not tried it isolated from the tea or any other supplements that have been recommended to increase supply. If you do decide to try this herb, once your milk increases it is encouraged for you to discontinue usage of the herb.

Myth: Size Doesn't Matter

It is often quoted "size doesn't matter." Well, in the world of pumping it does! You should make sure that your flanges (the funnel looking things that connect to the tubes) are the correct size, because size has a direct effect on your milk expression. If your flanges are too big or too small, you may not be expressing milk properly and may be incorrectly interpreting a low milk supply. The wrong size flanges could also lead to discomfort while pumping. It is a myth that pumping should be a little painful. Pumping should be as comfortable as possible. Make sure that you find the right flange that is best for you and fits your nipple size. Think about the flange like a pair of shoes. You would not walk around uncomfortable with shoes too big or too small, so don't settle with your flanges.

Health Risk/
Issues with Pumping

As mentioned previously, there are some issues related with pumping that can affect both your milk supply and your breast pumping experience. Here are two key terms as well as symptoms, causes, and treatment:

Engorgement: the buildup of milk and fluids in the breast occurring when breast become too full.

Engorgement Symptoms: Hard, swollen, or uncomfortable to touch (painful) breast

Causes:

- Overproduction

- Missing pumping/nursing sessions

- Not adequately draining breast

Treatment:

- Pump more frequently including after nursing

- Hand express breast milk

- Apply a warm compress to your breast before pumping

Mastitis: inflammation of breast tissue (milk ducts and glands

Symptoms of Mastitis: Sore tender breast, swelling (engorgement), red lumps on breast from clogged ducts, flu-like symptoms, tiredness, sharp pain, fever.

Causes:

- Improper Latch/ Baby having tongue-tie

- Clogged/blocked milk ducts

- Improper fitting bra

- Not adequately draining breast

- Engorgement

- Stress and lack of rest

Treatment:

- Pump more frequently including after nursing

- Rest

- Antibiotics if there is an infection

- Proper fitting bras

- Warm compress

- Hand expression

- Proper hydration

Breast Pump Reviews:

The Most Recommended Pumps for Exclusively Pumping Mamas

Since you've decided to exclusively pump or will be pumping most of the time, make sure that you have the right pump to meet your pumping needs. There are tons of options that range in prices and there is certainly one out there that will meet your specific pumping goals.

I've been able to use three electrical pumps over my last year of pumping. I've used the Medela Symphony (Hospital Grade Pump), the Ameda Purely Yours and the Medela Freestyle. Of course the hospital grade Medela was the best but the price tag on it was incredible so I won't even review that one! If you're interested in this high-grade pump, though, you can rent it from companies online.

The Ameda Purely Yours was the pump I used for the first six months. I loved the suction on it. It was small, compact and had the option to use batteries which was great for traveling and pumping. The pump, like many, was extremely loud and by month six I was convinced that the pump was talking to me each time I pumped due to the noise it made.

The Medela Freestyle was a pump that I purchased out of pocket. I absolutely loved it! I could put the pump in my pocket or on my waist like a pager and walk around pumping! The pump comes with a rechargeable battery pack, so you don't have to worry about paying for batteries. One of the major issues I had with the pump is the loudness. The noise level is about an eight on a scale of 1 to 10. This can be bad when you're pumping at night and don't want to wake the baby. But I'd definitely give it a 10 for convenience.

I've tried some manual pumps as well and found that some of them are a two on a scale of 1 to 10. The Medela and the Evenflo manual pumps were the two that were top rated for me but the Medela was number one. The Medela suction was better and the parts were easier to clean. I've also tried the Haakaa Silicon Breast pump which didn't work out for me. It was a little too much work for the little drops of milk that were extracted. I have noticed that the reviews for the Haaka pump are pretty good online and it may work out for you if you decide to try it. Please note, if time is of the essence, it may not be best to use a manual pump. However, if you have time to sit and extract milk at a slower pace, manual is the way to go. I honestly believe that the manual pump does well at emptying out the breast, even more so than the electric pumps do.

Choosing the best pump is important and you have options to choose the best one that works for you. Your pump will be by your side for however long you decide to use it, so make sure that your companion is one that you like. You have a choice in the matter!

Questions and Answers

Since I've been deemed the go to mama for women who are pumping I've been asked some questions that I feel many mama's want to ask.

What's the deal with Power Pumping?

Power pumping is a method used by women when they are trying to increase their milk supply. It is not a guaranteed method for ALL women but I have seen great results for women who have used this method. To begin, choose a time when you are available to dedicate at least one hour to power pumping. I have listed a guide to power pumping below:

Pump 20 mins	Rest 10 Mins
Pump 10 mins	Rest 10 Mins
Pump 10 mins	
Total 60 mins	

This guide can also be used when pumping one breast at a time, start with 10 minutes on each side instead of 20. If you do not see immediate results, you can increase the sessions but I would not recommend exceeding 3 power pumping sessions per day.

Are there any foods that help increase milk supply?

As stated in a previous chapter, there are foods that may help to increase your supply. These foods include but are not limited to Almonds, Calcium, Salmon, Oatmeal, Basil Leaves, Beet Leaves, Chickpeas,

Avocado, Leafy Greens, Lean Red Meat, Eggs, and Legumes/Beans. Each of these foods have been known to assist in boosting your milk supply. Try incorporating them into your diet if you have issues with your supply.

How do I go from Exclusively Nursing to Incorporating Pumping?

I'd say start slow and steady!

1. Pump while nursing: Pump the alternate breast while nursing so that by the time you've finished nursing, you've also finished pumping. There may be times that your pumping time exceeds your nursing time and you can decide if you want to continue pumping beyond the time of your little one's feeding.

2. Pump after nursing: this requires a great deal of discipline because it will require you to sit for additional time after your baby has been fed.

3. Create a pumping session between feedings, this can be a power pumping session of a regular session which will last 10-15 mins. This will get your body acclimated to the pump.

Can I put breastmilk in the refrigerator and then freeze it?

According to the CDC, breastmilk can be stored up to 4 days in the refrigerator however I would not recommend leaving it in the refrigerator for that long because it will begin to breakdown and have an odor to it that your little one my not like. I have taken my breastmilk out of the refrigerator within 72 hours and put it in the freezer for storage for 6-12 months.

Is it possible for me to breastfeed after I have had a breast implant?

It is very possible to pump after having breast implants. Just make sure that you use caution with the flanges as they may cause damage to the incisions and irritate the scar tissue from the augmentation.

How do I ween from the pump?

Don't go cold turkey! Take your time, it's almost like weening your baby from nursing so it takes determination because it can be a painful process. To begin, it is important to drop pumping sessions one at a time. If you are use to pumping 6 times a day decrease your session to 5 and decrease the time that you pump. If you are a person that gets engorged, make sure that you do not decrease sessions to fast as it can be very painful. When you get down to one pumping session a day, it may be safe to say that you can stop pumping. At this point you should not be getting as much milk and your body should be ready to stop.

If I increase the speed of my pump will I get more milk?

Increasing the speed of your pump does not guarantee more milk but it could damage your nipples and cause pain. Increasing the time of your pumping sessions may be more beneficial than increasing the speed of your pump.

How Much Milk Should I Be Producing?

Your body generally will produce what your baby needs. If you think that you're not getting enough milk there are some indicators that you can check which include your baby's weight gain/loss, the number of wet diapers your baby has per day (should be 6 to 10) and the amount/color of your baby's stool.

Why am I not getting as much milk as the other women I see on Social Media/YouTube/Blogs?

Every woman is different and so is her baby. Your body's production of milk is tailored to your baby's needs and is not to be compared with another woman's body. Don't get caught up with comparing your supply to a woman who has a large freezer stash. Admire her stash and keep it moving. Your baby will have just enough!

Take it Easy Mama! We all have tons of questions about being a mama and want to do what is best for our baby's. Make sure that you are taking care of yourself and that self-care is on your agenda.

The Saga Continues

I had vowed to be done pumping when my baby turned one and I even started to count down the days! I was honestly tired of pumping, cleaning pump parts, carrying the pump with me everywhere, and not forgetting that I needed the pump as much as I needed my car keys. However, I wanted to make sure that when I wrote this book, I had one year of exclusive pumping experience and not just a few months!

One day I began pumping and I became extremely nauseous. I had no clue what was going on or why. Had I built an intolerance to my pump? I began to question myself and try to figure out why I was so nauseous each pumping session? The nausea caused me to decrease my pumping because the thought of pumping and the actual act made me so sick to my stomach. I told one of my friends and she said she use to have those feelings early on during her pumping but they subsided. I understood what she was explaining, but I knew something was different for me. I knew my cycle would be coming very soon but I didn't know the exact date. The easiest thing I could do was rule out the other option of "pregnancy," so I decided to take a test. I went to Target (by now you can see that's my favorite place to be) got a two-pack test and went into the bathroom to take it. I'd never seen a test that took so long to give you the results. The results were "negative" and I was able to rule that out.

I continued to pump with extreme nausea for another week. By this point my milk production was very low. I wasn't even getting four complete ounces. A few days later after a morning pump session, I decided to take another pregnancy test. I took the test and waited, and waited, and waited. I really don't understand why those tests take so long to give you the results. As I waited, the test line began to get bold and I just knew it would be a negative reading. I looked up in the mirror for a moment and looked back down at the test. I couldn't believe what I was seeing… there were two lines on the test, I was pregnant again. Oh my goodness,

I did not know how this happened (just kidding I did know how) just not when. I really could not believe my eyes… I ran out of the bathroom and rushed up the steps to tell my sleeping husband the news, we were going to have another little baby! The excitement was unreal, my poor husband was awakened from his sleep to hear that we were expecting again. He was as surprised as I was! I was four days away from my first baby turning one and putting the pump to rest and now I was finding out that in a few months I would be starting the process all over again.

Reality began to set in as I continued to pump over the next four days. I realized that I had become attached to my pump and I did not want to let it go so fast. We had been doing life together for a while and it was not an easy habit to break. I have heard other mamas say it is hard to wean the baby and I agree and understand their sentiments. I hadn't been actually breastfeeding but my baby was receiving the same benefits from my breastmilk and it was so rewarding to say the least. I know at the beginning of this chapter I told you I was anxious to let go of the pump, but when it was time I wasn't ready. So what did I decide to do? I decided to keep going until I was ready to stop. When I was ready, one of the contributing factors that assisted me in not pumping any longer was the fact that my supply did not increase but instead diminished. I am still not sure why this happened, maybe the new baby needed those nutrients. I tried supplements, mostly oatmeal, but nothing really helped.

When I made first doctor's appointment to confirm pregnancy, I let her know that I was still pumping. I was advised that if I wanted to continue pumping that I should consider stopping around week 22 because the stimulation could induce contractions. When I left the doctor's office, I had so much to consider and I decided to "pump wean" (I made that up). I began to decrease my pumping until I completely stopped. I had a stash of milk to give to my baby which would last for a little while and then I would have to decide what milk options were available for my little one.

There's always a decision to make and I've realized that you have to make the best one for you and your little one who is depending on you. One of the best decisions I've ever made was to be a Pumping Mama and I want to encourage you, even when it gets hard and you feel alone, you have mamas around the world rooting for you. Pump, Mama, Pump!

Love Notes to your Baby While Pumping

(Take a Moment to Write a Few Notes to your Little One)

There's No Love Like A Mother's Love

_____

_____

_____

Pump Mama Pump

Love in a Bottle One Ounce at a Time

Pump Mama Pump

_____

_____

_____

_____

_____

_____

_____

_____

It's my Joy to Share with You

Pump Mama Pump

You are My Sunshine My Only Sunshine

Pump Mama Pump

Never Forget How Much You are Loved

Pump Mama Pump

_____

_____

_____

_____

_____

_____

_____

Pump Mama Pump

Diary

Date:	Date:	Date:
Pumping Time Start/Finish: Volume:	Pumping Time Start/Finish: Volume:	Pumping Time Start/Finish: Volume:

Pump Mama Pump

Daily Total (in oz):	Daily Total (in oz):	Daily Total (in oz):
Power Pumping Session? Yes/No	Power Pumping Session? Yes/No	Power Pumping Session? Yes/No
Daily Diet/Intake: Daily Water Intake (8oz cups): 1 2 3 4 5 6 7 8 9 10	Daily Diet/Intake: Daily Water Intake (8oz cups): 1 2 3 4 5 6 7 8 9 10	Daily Diet/Intake: Daily Water Intake (8oz cups): 1 2 3 4 5 6 7 8 9 10

Pump Mama Pump

Diary

Date:	Date:	Date:
Pumping Time Start/Finish: Volume:	Pumping Time Start/Finish: Volume:	Pumping Time Start/Finish: Volume:

Daily Total (in oz):	Daily Total (in oz):	Daily Total (in oz):
Power Pumping Session? Yes/No	Power Pumping Session? Yes/No	Power Pumping Session? Yes/No
Daily Diet/Intake:	Daily Diet/Intake:	Daily Diet/Intake:
Daily Water Intake (8oz cups): 1 2 3 4 5 6 7 8 9 10	Daily Water Intake (8oz cups): 1 2 3 4 5 6 7 8 9 10	Daily Water Intake (8oz cups): 1 2 3 4 5 6 7 8 9 10

Pump Mama Pump

Diary

Date:	Date:	Date:
Pumping Time Start/Finish: Volume:	Pumping Time Start/Finish: Volume:	Pumping Time Start/Finish: Volume:

Daily Total (in oz):	Daily Total (in oz):	Daily Total (in oz):
Power Pumping Session? Yes/No	Power Pumping Session? Yes/No	Power Pumping Session? Yes/No
Daily Diet/Intake:	Daily Diet/Intake:	Daily Diet/Intake:
Daily Water Intake (8oz cups): 1 2 3 4 5 6 7 8 9 10	Daily Water Intake (8oz cups): 1 2 3 4 5 6 7 8 9 10	Daily Water Intake (8oz cups): 1 2 3 4 5 6 7 8 9 10

Pump Mama Pump

Diary

Date:	Date:	Date:
Pumping Time Start/Finish: Volume:	Pumping Time Start/Finish: Volume:	Pumping Time Start/Finish: Volume:

Daily Total (in oz):	Daily Total (in oz):	Daily Total (in oz):
Power Pumping Session? Yes/No	Power Pumping Session? Yes/No	Power Pumping Session? Yes/No
Daily Diet/Intake:	Daily Diet/Intake:	Daily Diet/Intake:
Daily Water Intake (8oz cups): 1 2 3 4 5 6 7 8 9 10	Daily Water Intake (8oz cups): 1 2 3 4 5 6 7 8 9 10	Daily Water Intake (8oz cups): 1 2 3 4 5 6 7 8 9 10

Pump Mama Pump

Diary

Date:	Date:	Date:
Pumping Time Start/Finish: Volume:	Pumping Time Start/Finish: Volume:	Pumping Time Start/Finish: Volume:

Daily Total (in oz):	Daily Total (in oz):	Daily Total (in oz):
Power Pumping Session? Yes/No	Power Pumping Session? Yes/No	Power Pumping Session? Yes/No
Daily Diet/Intake:	Daily Diet/Intake:	Daily Diet/Intake:
Daily Water Intake (8oz cups): 1 2 3 4 5 6 7 8 9 10	Daily Water Intake (8oz cups): 1 2 3 4 5 6 7 8 9 10	Daily Water Intake (8oz cups): 1 2 3 4 5 6 7 8 9 10

Pump Mama Pump

Diary

Date:	Date:	Date:
Pumping Time Start/Finish: Volume:	Pumping Time Start/Finish: Volume:	Pumping Time Start/Finish: Volume:

Pump Mama Pump

Daily Total (in oz):	Daily Total (in oz):	Daily Total (in oz):
Power Pumping Session? Yes/No	Power Pumping Session? Yes/No	Power Pumping Session? Yes/No
Daily Diet/Intake:	Daily Diet/Intake:	Daily Diet/Intake:
Daily Water Intake (8oz cups): 1 2 3 4 5 6 7 8 9 10	Daily Water Intake (8oz cups): 1 2 3 4 5 6 7 8 9 10	Daily Water Intake (8oz cups): 1 2 3 4 5 6 7 8 9 10

Pump Mama Pump

Diary

Date:	Date:	Date:
Pumping Time Start/Finish: Volume:	Pumping Time Start/Finish: Volume:	Pumping Time Start/Finish: Volume:

Daily Total (in oz):	Daily Total (in oz):	Daily Total (in oz):
Power Pumping Session? Yes/No	Power Pumping Session? Yes/No	Power Pumping Session? Yes/No
Daily Diet/Intake:	Daily Diet/Intake:	Daily Diet/Intake:
Daily Water Intake (8oz cups): 1 2 3 4 5 6 7 8 9 10	Daily Water Intake (8oz cups): 1 2 3 4 5 6 7 8 9 10	Daily Water Intake (8oz cups): 1 2 3 4 5 6 7 8 9 10

Pump Mama Pump

Diary

Date:	Date:	Date:
Pumping Time Start/Finish: Volume:	Pumping Time Start/Finish: Volume:	Pumping Time Start/Finish: Volume:

Daily Total (in oz):	Daily Total (in oz):	Daily Total (in oz):
Power Pumping Session? Yes/No	Power Pumping Session? Yes/No	Power Pumping Session? Yes/No
Daily Diet/Intake:	Daily Diet/Intake:	Daily Diet/Intake:
Daily Water Intake (8oz cups): 1 2 3 4 5 6 7 8 9 10	Daily Water Intake (8oz cups): 1 2 3 4 5 6 7 8 9 10	Daily Water Intake (8oz cups): 1 2 3 4 5 6 7 8 9 10

Pump Mama Pump

Diary

Date:	Date:	Date:
Pumping Time Start/Finish: Volume:	Pumping Time Start/Finish: Volume:	Pumping Time Start/Finish: Volume:

Daily Total (in oz):	Daily Total (in oz):	Daily Total (in oz):
Power Pumping Session? Yes/No	Power Pumping Session? Yes/No	Power Pumping Session? Yes/No
Daily Diet/Intake:	Daily Diet/Intake:	Daily Diet/Intake:
Daily Water Intake (8oz cups): 1 2 3 4 5 6 7 8 9 10	Daily Water Intake (8oz cups): 1 2 3 4 5 6 7 8 9 10	Daily Water Intake (8oz cups): 1 2 3 4 5 6 7 8 9 10

Pump Mama Pump

Diary

Date:	Date:	Date:
Pumping Time Start/Finish: Volume:	Pumping Time Start/Finish: Volume:	Pumping Time Start/Finish: Volume:

Daily Total (in oz):	Daily Total (in oz):	Daily Total (in oz):
Power Pumping Session? Yes/No	Power Pumping Session? Yes/No	Power Pumping Session? Yes/No
Daily Diet/Intake:	Daily Diet/Intake:	Daily Diet/Intake:
Daily Water Intake (8oz cups): 1 2 3 4 5 6 7 8 9 10	Daily Water Intake (8oz cups): 1 2 3 4 5 6 7 8 9 10	Daily Water Intake (8oz cups): 1 2 3 4 5 6 7 8 9 10

Pump Mama Pump

Diary

Date:	Date:	Date:
Pumping Time Start/Finish: Volume:	Pumping Time Start/Finish: Volume:	Pumping Time Start/Finish: Volume:

Daily Total (in oz):	Daily Total (in oz):	Daily Total (in oz):
Power Pumping Session? Yes/No	Power Pumping Session? Yes/No	Power Pumping Session? Yes/No
Daily Diet/Intake:	Daily Diet/Intake:	Daily Diet/Intake:
Daily Water Intake (8oz cups): 1 2 3 4 5 6 7 8 9 10	Daily Water Intake (8oz cups): 1 2 3 4 5 6 7 8 9 10	Daily Water Intake (8oz cups): 1 2 3 4 5 6 7 8 9 10

Pump Mama Pump

Diary

Date:	Date:	Date:
Pumping Time Start/Finish: Volume:	Pumping Time Start/Finish: Volume:	Pumping Time Start/Finish: Volume:

Daily Total (in oz):	Daily Total (in oz):	Daily Total (in oz):
Power Pumping Session? Yes/No	Power Pumping Session? Yes/No	Power Pumping Session? Yes/No
Daily Diet/Intake:	Daily Diet/Intake:	Daily Diet/Intake:
Daily Water Intake (8oz cups): 1 2 3 4 5 6 7 8 9 10	Daily Water Intake (8oz cups): 1 2 3 4 5 6 7 8 9 10	Daily Water Intake (8oz cups): 1 2 3 4 5 6 7 8 9 10

Pump Mama Pump

Diary

Date:	Date:	Date:
Pumping Time Start/Finish: Volume:	Pumping Time Start/Finish: Volume:	Pumping Time Start/Finish: Volume:

Pump Mama Pump

Daily Total (in oz):	Daily Total (in oz):	Daily Total (in oz):
Power Pumping Session? Yes/No	Power Pumping Session? Yes/No	Power Pumping Session? Yes/No
Daily Diet/Intake:	Daily Diet/Intake:	Daily Diet/Intake:
Daily Water Intake (8oz cups): 1 2 3 4 5 6 7 8 9 10	Daily Water Intake (8oz cups): 1 2 3 4 5 6 7 8 9 10	Daily Water Intake (8oz cups): 1 2 3 4 5 6 7 8 9 10

Pump Mama Pump

Diary

Date:	Date:	Date:
Pumping Time Start/Finish: Volume:	Pumping Time Start/Finish: Volume:	Pumping Time Start/Finish: Volume:

Daily Total (in oz):	Daily Total (in oz):	Daily Total (in oz):
Power Pumping Session? Yes/No	Power Pumping Session? Yes/No	Power Pumping Session? Yes/No
Daily Diet/Intake:	Daily Diet/Intake:	Daily Diet/Intake:
Daily Water Intake (8oz cups): 1 2 3 4 5 6 7 8 9 10	Daily Water Intake (8oz cups): 1 2 3 4 5 6 7 8 9 10	Daily Water Intake (8oz cups): 1 2 3 4 5 6 7 8 9 10

Pump Mama Pump

Diary

Date:	Date:	Date:
Pumping Time Start/Finish: Volume:	Pumping Time Start/Finish: Volume:	Pumping Time Start/Finish: Volume:

Pump Mama Pump

Daily Total (in oz):	Daily Total (in oz):	Daily Total (in oz):
Power Pumping Session? Yes/No	Power Pumping Session? Yes/No	Power Pumping Session? Yes/No
Daily Diet/Intake:	Daily Diet/Intake:	Daily Diet/Intake:
Daily Water Intake (8oz cups): 1 2 3 4 5 6 7 8 9 10	Daily Water Intake (8oz cups): 1 2 3 4 5 6 7 8 9 10	Daily Water Intake (8oz cups): 1 2 3 4 5 6 7 8 9 10

Pump Mama Pump

Diary

Date:	Date:	Date:
Pumping Time Start/Finish: Volume:	Pumping Time Start/Finish: Volume:	Pumping Time Start/Finish: Volume:

Daily Total (in oz):	Daily Total (in oz):	Daily Total (in oz):
Power Pumping Session? Yes/No	Power Pumping Session? Yes/No	Power Pumping Session? Yes/No
Daily Diet/Intake:	Daily Diet/Intake:	Daily Diet/Intake:
Daily Water Intake (8oz cups): 1 2 3 4 5 6 7 8 9 10	Daily Water Intake (8oz cups): 1 2 3 4 5 6 7 8 9 10	Daily Water Intake (8oz cups): 1 2 3 4 5 6 7 8 9 10

Pump Mama Pump

Diary

Date:	Date:	Date:
Pumping Time Start/Finish: Volume:	Pumping Time Start/Finish: Volume:	Pumping Time Start/Finish: Volume:

Daily Total (in oz):	Daily Total (in oz):	Daily Total (in oz):
Power Pumping Session? Yes/No	Power Pumping Session? Yes/No	Power Pumping Session? Yes/No
Daily Diet/Intake:	Daily Diet/Intake:	Daily Diet/Intake:
Daily Water Intake (8oz cups): 1 2 3 4 5 6 7 8 9 10	Daily Water Intake (8oz cups): 1 2 3 4 5 6 7 8 9 10	Daily Water Intake (8oz cups): 1 2 3 4 5 6 7 8 9 10

Made in the USA
Middletown, DE
18 August 2019